Daily Warm-Ups
PRE-ALGEBRA
Common Core State Standards

Betsy Berry, Ph.D.

Indiana University–Purdue University Fort Wayne

1   2   3   4   5   6   7   8   9   10
ISBN 978-0-8251-6884-0
Copyright © 2012
J. Weston Walch, Publisher
40 Walch Drive • Portland, ME 04103
www.walch.com
Printed in the United States of America

Table of Contents

Daily Warm-Ups: Pre-Algebra, Common Core State Standards

Introduction

Daily Warm-Ups: Pre-Algebra for Common Core State Standards is organized into nine sections, composed of the following domains for grades 4–8 designated by the Common Core State Standards Initiative: Operations and Algebraic Thinking (Grade 4); Number and Operations—Fractions (Grades 4–5); Measurement and Data (Grade 4); Ratios and Proportional Relationships (Grades 6–7); The Number System (Grades 6–8); Expressions and Equations (Grades 6–8); Functions (Grade 8); Geometry (Grades 6–8); and Statistics and Probability (Grades 7–8). Each warm-up addresses one or more of the standards within these domains.

The Common Core Mathematical Practices standards are another focus of the warm-ups. All of the problems require students to "make sense of problems and persevere in solving them," "reason abstractly and quantitatively," and "attend to precision." Many of the warm-ups ask students to "look for and express regularity in repeated reasoning" when generating functions to symbolize patterns or rules. Students must "look for and make use of structure" when finding the lowest common denominator in applications of addition and subtraction of fractions. Several problems require the use of a coordinate grid. This provides students the opportunity to "use appropriate tools strategically." A full description of these standards can be found at www.corestandards.org/Math/Practice/.

The warm-ups are organized by domains rather than by level of difficulty. Use your judgment to select appropriate problems for your students.* The problems are not meant to be completed in consecutive order—some are stand-alone, some can launch a topic, some can be used as journal prompts, and some refresh students' skills and concepts. All are meant to enhance and complement pre-algebra programs. They do so by providing resources for teachers for those short, 5-to-15-minute interims when class time might otherwise go unused.

*You may select warm-ups based on particular standards using the Standards Correlations document on the accompanying CD.

About the CD-ROM

Daily Warm-Ups: Pre-Algebra, Common Core State Standards is provided in two convenient formats: an easy-to-use reproducible book and a ready-to-print PDF on a companion CD-ROM.
You can photocopy or print activities as needed, or project them on a screen via your computer.

The depth and breadth of the collection give you the opportunity to choose specific skills and concepts that correspond to your curriculum and instruction. The activities address the following Common Core State Standards for grades 4–8 mathematics: Operations and Algebraic Thinking (Grade 4); Number and Operations—Fractions (Grades 4–5); Measurement and Data (Grade 4); Ratios and Proportional Relationships (Grades 6–7); The Number System (Grades 6–8); Expressions and Equations (Grades 6–8); Functions (Grade 8); Geometry (Grades 6–8); and Statistics and Probability (Grades 7–8). Use the table of contents, the title pages, and the standards correlations provided on the CD-ROM to help you select appropriate tasks.

Suggestions for use:

- Choose an activity to project or print out and assign.
- Select a series of activities. Print the selection to create practice packets for learners who need help with specific skills or concepts.

Daily Warm-Ups: Pre- Algebra, Common Core State Standards

Part 1: Operations and Algebraic Thinking

Overview

Grade 4

- Use the four operations with whole numbers to solve problems.
- Gain familiarity with factors and multiples.

Perfect Numbers

A number is said to be perfect if it is equal to the sum of all its proper factors. Proper factors are all the factors of the number including 1, except for the number itself. Find three numbers that are perfect and show why they are perfect numbers using the definition given.

Stacking T-shirts

A clerk in a sportswear department was asked to arrange T-shirts in a display in stacks of equal size. When she separated the T-shirts into stacks of 4, there was 1 left over. When she tried stacks of 5, there was still 1 left over. The same was true for stacks of 6. However, she was able to arrange the shirts evenly in stacks of 7. How many T-shirts were in the display that she was arranging?

2

Rectangular Configurations

Washington Center Junior Chamber of Commerce is hosting a holiday craft show. They are renting spaces in a variety of rectangular configurations with side lengths that are whole numbers. The spaces are between 30 and 50 square yards.

1. Which number(s) of square yards, between 30 and 50, give the most choices for rectangular arrangements? Why?

2. Which number(s) of square yards, between 30 and 50, allow for square spaces to rent? Why? Explain your thinking.

Planting Evergreen Trees

Garrett works on a tree farm where they just received a shipment of 144 seedlings. He wants to plant rows of trees in a rectangular pattern. How many different rectangular configurations can he make? What are they? Explain your thinking.

4

Part 2: Number and Operations—Fractions

Overview

Grade 4

- Extend understanding of fraction equivalence and ordering.

Grade 5

- Use equivalent fractions as a strategy to add and subtract fractions.
- Apply and extend previous understandings of multiplication and division to multiply and divide fractions.

Comparing Fractions

Jordan, Jose, and Brigit are comparing the sizes of the fractions $\frac{7}{8}$ and $\frac{2}{3}$. Jordan is using fraction strips, Jose is using graph paper, and Brigit is using decimal equivalences. Explain with pictures, diagrams, calculations, and words how each of them can demonstrate which value is larger.

Fraction Sense

1. Name two fractions that come between $\frac{3}{5}$ and $\frac{4}{5}$. Justify your answer in two or more different ways.

2. Which of the following fractions is larger: $\frac{8}{9}$ or $\frac{11}{12}$? Explain how you can determine which fraction is larger without changing the fractions to decimals or finding a common denominator.

6

Right or Wrong?

Max is looking over his younger sister's math homework. He notices that she wrote the following:

$$\frac{3}{4} + \frac{2}{3} = \frac{5}{7}$$

Without doing any calculations, he tells her that this is an incorrect math sentence. Is he right? What might he be thinking? How could he explain his reasoning to his sister?

7

Bigger or Smaller?

Shanita and Leon are discussing their math homework. Leon says, "When you multiply one number by another number, the result is always bigger than the number you started with. When you divide one number by another number, the result is always smaller than the number you started with." Is Leon's statement always true? Can you give examples in which the statement is true and other examples in which the statement is false?

8

Part 3: Measurement and Data

Overview

Grade 4

- Solve problems involving measurement and conversion of measurements from a larger unit to a smaller unit.

Buying Carpet

1. Todd and Maria are renovating their home. Their living room is a rectangle that measures 15 feet wide and 21 feet long. They are looking at new carpet that is on sale for $7.32 per square yard. How much will it cost to install this carpet in their living room?

2. They also want to install baseboard molding in the living room after the carpeting is done. The molding they want costs $134.00 per 8-foot piece. How much should they buy, and what will it cost?

9

Sketching Rectangles

Using grid paper, sketch all the rectangles you can find that have an area of 48 square units. How many different rectangles did you find? What is the perimeter of each rectangle? Which rectangle has the smallest perimeter? Which has the largest? Did you find a rectangle that is a perfect square? Why or why not?

10

Raising Zebra Finches

Kanya and her father raise and breed zebra finches. They have an aviary made of wood and wire mesh that measures 6 feet wide by 4 feet deep by 5 feet high. Their manual says that every pair of finches should have 3 to 4 square feet of area. The height of the space may vary. Kanya and her father now have 5 pairs of finches in the cage. They would like to expand their flock to a total of 12 pairs of birds. Do they have enough space for the 5 pairs they have now? They want to keep their finches happy and have decided to provide the maximum space for them. How could they increase the size of the cage to make space for 12 pairs? How much more wire mesh will they need to enclose their new aviary? (They do not put the wire mesh on the floor of the cage, but they cover all other sides with it.)

11

Part 4: Ratios and Proportional Relationships

Overview

Grade 6

- Understand ratio concepts and use ratio reasoning to solve problems.

Grade 7

- Analyze proportional relationships and use them to solve real-world and mathematical problems.

Birthday Roses

Alonzo is planning to purchase roses for his mother on her birthday. He has seen them advertised at 12 roses for $15.00 and 20 roses for $23.00. Which is the better buy?

12

Square Pizza

Lin, Lon, Lu, and Lau have ordered a pizza from the Tip Top Pizza Palace. The pizzas only come in one size and are in the shape of a square. Lau has just had a blueberry smoothie and is not very hungry, but she thinks that she might eat 10% of the pizza. Lon is famished and thinks that he might eat half of the pizza. Lin thinks she might eat about 35% of the pizza, and Lu thinks he might eat 15%. If the four friends eat the portions that they have predicted, what percent of the pizza will remain? Justify your thinking using a 10 × 10 grid like the one below.

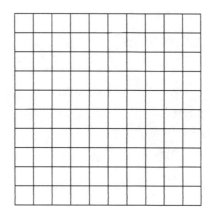

Paolo's Pizza Pricing

Paolo has just started working at his Uncle Antonio's pizza parlor. He is trying to figure out which size meat lover's pizza provides the best value.

Meat Lover's Special

9-inch round pizza...................$10.50
12-inch round pizza.................$15.00
18-inch round pizza..................$19.00

Which pizza listed on the menu provides the best value? Write a few sentences that explain your reasoning.

14

Balancing a Milk Bottle

An American named Ashrita Furman holds more Guinness World Records than any other person. In April 1998, he walked 81 miles in 23 hours, 35 minutes while balancing a milk bottle on his head. How fast did he walk in miles per hour?

15

Vanishing Wetlands

Bonita works for the Desoto Park Service. The Little Otter Wetland Area that she monitors has had drought conditions recently. She is preparing a report on the drought for the park service. The grid below represents a model for the change in area of the wetland. What was the percent change in wetland area from August 2010 to August 2011? Explain your thinking.

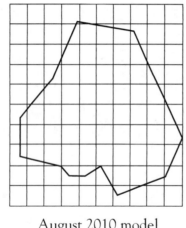

August 2010 model

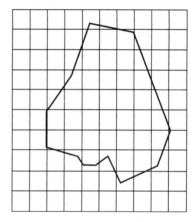

August 2011 model

16

Percent Increase or Decrease

Look at the sequences below. For each, tell whether there is growth or decay, identify the common ratio, and give the percent increase or decrease.

1. 43, 129, 387, 1,161, . . .

2. 90, 99, 108.9, 119.79, . . .

3. 1,800, 1,080, 648, 388.8, . . .

4. 17.8, 3.56, 0.712, 0.1424, . . .

5. 375, 142.5, 54.15, 20.577, . . .

17

Bread Prices

1. According to the U.S. Bureau of Labor Statistics, a loaf of white bread cost $0.79 in 1995 and $1.04 in 2005. What is the percent increase in price for this 10-year period?

2. If the trend continues, what would be the predicted price for a loaf of white bread in 2015?

3. If the price in 2010 was $1.37, is the trend continuing at the same percentage rate? Explain your thinking.

18

Part 5: The Number System

Overview

Grade 6

- Apply and extend previous understandings of multiplication and division to divide fractions by fractions.
- Compute fluently with multi-digit numbers and find common factors and multiples.

Grade 7

- Apply and extend previous understandings of operations with fractions to add, subtract, multiply, and divide rational numbers.

Grade 8

- Know that there are numbers that are not rational, and approximate them by rational numbers.

Ribbon and Bows

Veronica is making decorative bows for a craft project. She has 7 yards of velvet ribbon. Each bow requires $\frac{3}{4}$ of a yard of ribbon. How many bows will she be able to make with the ribbon she has? Will she have any ribbon left? Explain your thinking.

19

Baking Blueberry Pies

Mrs. Berry is famous for her pies. She has been making pies in her bakery for many years. She knows that it takes $1\frac{2}{3}$ cups of flour to make her special pie crust. She buys flour in 25-pound bags and knows that each pound contains about 3 cups of flour. How many pies can she expect to make from a 25-pound bag of flour?

20

Super Sub Sandwich

The students at Abigail Adams Middle School tried to make the biggest sub sandwich on record. They made a sandwich that was $12\frac{3}{4}$ feet long. After they were told that this did not break the record, they decided to divide the sandwich into smaller portions and share it with other students.

1. If each portion was $\frac{1}{2}$ foot long, how many students would get a portion?

2. If each portion was $\frac{3}{4}$ foot long, how many students would get a portion?

3. Explain and illustrate your thinking using a diagram.

21

© 2012 Walch Education

What Day of the Week?

Saari and Anatole are cooped up inside because of bad weather. Their mother, a middle-school teacher, poses a puzzler for them. She says that Anatole was born 759 days after Saari, with no leap year between the two birthdays. If Saari was born on a Wednesday, on what day of the week was Anatole born? Find the day of the week and explain your strategy for finding it.

22

Greatest Common Factor

Find the greatest common factor (GCF) of 360, 336, and 1,260. Describe the strategy you used to find the GCF. Will your strategy work for all situations?

23

Library Day

Marika, Bobbie, and Claude all visit their local public library on a regular schedule. Marika visits every 15 days, Bobbie goes every 12 days, and Claude goes every 25 days. If they are all at the library today, in how many days from now will they all be there again? What strategy did you use to find the number of days? What does your answer represent?

24

Cicada Cycles

Cicadas are insects that eat plants. Stephan's grandfather told him that some cicadas have 13-year or 17-year cycles. He said that one year, the cicadas were so numerous on his family farm that they ate all the crops. Stephan guessed that perhaps both the 13-year and the 17-year cicadas came out that year.

1. If we assume Stephan is correct, how many years will have passed when the 13-year and 17-year cicadas come out together again?

2. Imagine that there are 12-year, 14-year, and 16-year cicadas, and they all come out this year. How many years will pass before they all come out together again?

3. Explain how you got your answer. What number does your answer represent?

Make a True Sentence

For the sentence below, insert mathematical symbols of any kind to make the sentence true. It is possible to make 2- or 3-digit numbers by not inserting any symbols between the numbers (for instance, by putting 5 and 6 together to make 56).

1   2   3   4   5   6   7   8   9   =   100

26

Working with Integers 1

Using appropriate arrow notations on number lines such as the one pictured below, represent the expressions given and find the results. Use a new number line for each sentence.

1. $-8 + 12 = ?$

2. $(-7) + (-3) = ?$

3. $5 + (-9) = ?$

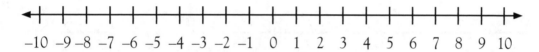

Working with Integers II

Look at each diagram below. Write a true sentence showing the integer calculations pictured.

1.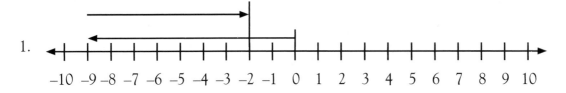

2.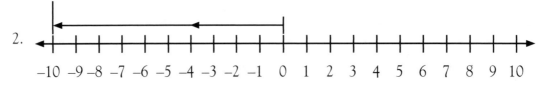

3.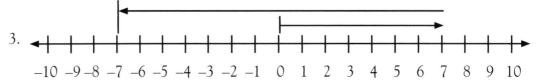

Chip-Board Integers I

Andrew and Brittany are exploring integers by drawing representations using black and white circular chips. The white chips represent positive numbers. The black chips represent negative numbers. Write a number sentence to symbolize each set of chip boards that they have drawn.

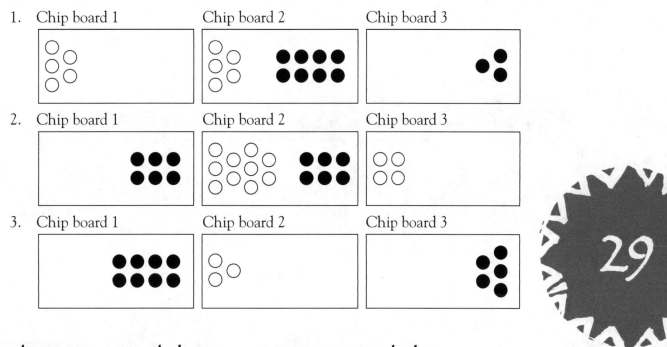

1. Chip board 1   Chip board 2   Chip board 3

2. Chip board 1   Chip board 2   Chip board 3

3. Chip board 1   Chip board 2   Chip board 3

29

Chip-Board Integers II

Diagram and solve the following integer operations. Use chip boards such as the ones pictured below. Use black circles, or chips, to represent negative values. Use white circles, or chips, to represent positive values. Use a series of two or three chip boards for each sentence.

1. $(-5) + (9) = ?$

2. $12 + (-7) = ?$

3. $(-8) - (-5) = ?$

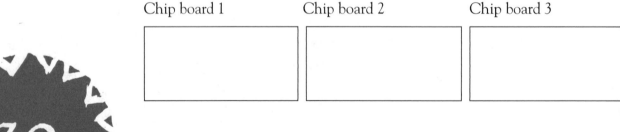

Chip board 1　　　Chip board 2　　　Chip board 3

30

Daily Warm-Ups: Pre-Algebra, Common Core State Standards

Chip-Board Integers III

Explain how you might show the operation $(-6) - (-12) = ?$ on a chip board or a series of chip boards such as the ones pictured below. Use black circles, or chips, to represent negative values. Use white circles, or chips, to represent positive values. A black chip and a white chip together represent zero.

Chip board 1

Chip board 2

Chip board 3

Integer Practice

Find the missing value in each sentence below.

1. $(-6) + (-12) = ?$

2. $25 - (-8) = ?$

3. $? + 17 = (-4)$

4. $11 + ? = 6$

5. $\dfrac{3}{4} - ? = 1$

6. $(-7) + ? = 0$

7. $2\dfrac{1}{2} + ? = \dfrac{1}{2}$

8. $? - (-5) = 0$

9. $-3.5 - \dfrac{7}{2} = ?$

10. $(-5.6) - ? = (-3.4)$

11. $? + 7\dfrac{2}{5} = 3\dfrac{3}{5}$

12. $-\dfrac{87}{10} + ? = 10$

32

Using 10 x 10 Grids 1

Adriana has shaded a portion of each 10×10 grid pictured below. What fraction of each has been shaded? Express the fraction as a decimal. What percent of each grid has been shaded?

1.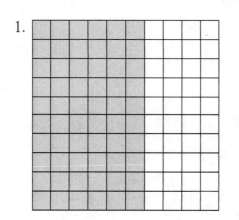

2.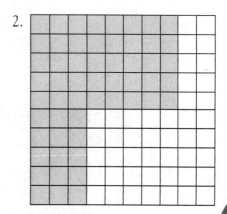

Using 10 x 10 Grids II

Micaela is learning about the connection between decimals and fractions. She has made the following diagram in her notes to represent multiplying decimals less than 1. What multiplication sentence(s) might be represented by the darker shaded area of her drawing?

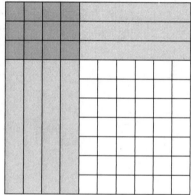

Four 4s

Express each of the numbers 1 through 10 using only the following: the addition, subtraction, multiplication, and division symbols; four 4s; and parentheses, if necessary.

35

Numbering Pages

Dylan used 2,989 digits to number the pages of a book. How many pages are in the book? Remember that digits are the symbols 0, 1, 2, 3, 4, 5, 6, 7, 8, 9. Explain how you got your answer.

36

A Circle of Students

Every year on the first day of spring, all the students at Thoreau Middle School stand in a perfect, evenly spaced circle on the athletic field in honor of the vernal equinox. This year, Taylor notices that she is in seventh place on the circle. Directly opposite her in position number 791 is her friend Mattie. How many students make up the circle this year?

Compressing Trash

According to the U.S. Environmental Protection Agency's 2003 report, every person generates an average of 4.6 pounds of garbage per day. Of this, approximately 25% is recycled. If a cubic foot of compressed garbage weighs about 50 pounds, how much space would be needed for the garbage generated by a family of four in one year?

38

Where Do They Go?

Using the number line below, show approximately where each number would fall. Explain your thinking.

1. $\sqrt{96}$
2. $\sqrt{35}$
3. $\sqrt{24}$
4. $\sqrt{17}$

39

Part 6: Expressions and Equations

Overview

Grade 6

- Apply and extend previous understandings of arithmetic to algebraic expressions.
- Reason about and solve one-variable equations and inequalities.

Grade 7

- Use properties of operations to generate equivalent expressions.

Grade 8

- Work with radicals and integer exponents.
- Analyze and solve linear equations and pairs of simultaneous linear equations.

A Number Puzzle

Choose any number. Add the number that is 1 more than your original number. Add 11. Divide by 2. Subtract your original number. What is your answer? Do the puzzle again for other numbers. Why do you get the answers that you get? Will this always work?

40

Collette's Chocolates

Collette works as the marketing manager for a small chocolate-making company. She has data that shows that the company's orange creams and French mints are the most recent best sellers. The French mints are a little more popular than the orange creams. Her supervisor has asked her to create new packaging for a Valentine's Day sales promotion. Collette has come up with the following plan for different-sized boxes of chocolates. The round shapes represent orange creams. The squares represent French mints.

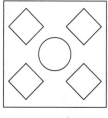

2 × 2 box

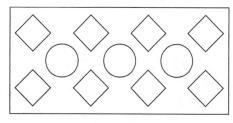

2 × 4 box

1. If Collette continues her pattern and she increases both the number of rows and/or the number of columns, what would a 4 × 6 box of chocolates look like? Draw several more boxes of chocolates that you think will continue Collette's design.

2. How many orange creams would be in the 4 × 6 box? Write a rule for finding the number of orange creams if you know the rows and columns of French mints.

41

Daily Warm-Ups: Pre-Algebra, Common Core State Standards

Evaluating Simple Expressions I

Evaluate each expression below for the given value of x.

1. $4.5x - 12$ for $x = 2$

2. $-5 - x$ for $x = \dfrac{1}{2}$

3. $2x^2$ for $x = 8$

4. $x^2 + 2.5$ for $x = 1.5$

5. $(x - 2.5)(x + 35)$ for $x = 2.5$

6. $x(27 - x)$ for $x = 3$

7. $\dfrac{49}{x^2}$ for $x = -7$

8. $5x^2 + 3x - 10$ for $x = 2$

9. $\dfrac{x}{4}$ for $x = 8$

10. $.5x^2 + 2x - 20$ for $x = 10$

42

Evaluating Simple Expressions II

Evaluate each expression below for the given value of x.

1. $42 - 3x$ for $x = 6$

2. $13 - 3x^2$ for $x = 1$

3. $4x^2 + 13$ for $x = -10$

4. $6x^2 + x - 2$ for $x = 2$

5. $(x - 2.5)(x + 5)$ for $x = 0$

6. $x(27 - x)$ for $x = -3$

7. $\dfrac{3(15 - x)}{2x}$ for $x = 10$

8. $8x - 3x(6 - x)$ for $x = 0$

9. $\dfrac{x^2}{4}(x + 8)$ for $x = -8$

10. $-2x^2 + 5x + 12$ for $x = -4$

43

Daily Warm-Ups: Pre-Algebra, Common Core State Standards

Border Tiles 1

Landscapers often use square tiles as borders for garden plots and pools. The drawing below represents a square pool for goldfish surrounded by 1-foot square tiles.

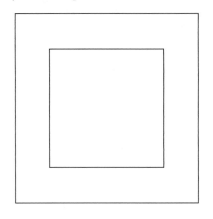

Maria thinks that the total number of tiles around the outside of the pool could be represented by $(n + 2) + (n + 2) + n + n$. Carlos thinks that he can represent the total number of tiles by $4(n + 1)$. What do you think about Carlos and Maria's representations? How do you think they would explain their thinking? Can you show if their expressions are equivalent or not?

Dividing by Fractions

Write a word problem that could result in the number sentence below. Then explain how you know it fits the sentence.

$$5 \div \frac{2}{3} = 7R\frac{1}{2}$$

45

Perimeter Problem

Use the figure on the right to answer the questions that follow.

1. If M = 5 meters, N = 4 meters, and L = 2.5 meters, what is the perimeter of the figure?

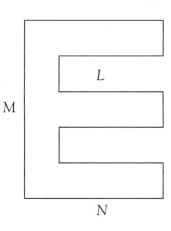

2. Using the variables only, write two or more expressions that could represent the perimeter of the figure. Show that your expressions are equivalent.

3. Is there another way to represent the perimeter of the figure?

Thinking Around the Box

The rectangular box shown below has a front and back length of L meters. The side lengths are W meters. The height is H meters.

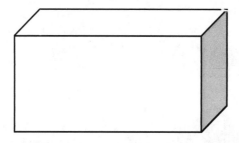

1. Write two equations that represent the sum, S, of all the edges of the rectangular box.

2. Write two equations that represent the surface area, A, of the rectangular box.

Simplifying Expressions

Write at least two more expressions that are equivalent to each given expression below.

1. $8(x - 5)$

2. $x(5x - 6) + 13x - 10$

3. $4(x + 5) - 3(2 - 4x)$

4. $2.5(12 - 2x) + 5(x + 1)$

5. $(3x^2 + 5x + 8) - (8x^2 + 2x - 5)$

48

Tearing and Stacking Paper

Mr. Andres poses the following problem to his math class: Take a large sheet of paper and tear it exactly in half. Then you have 2 sheets of paper. Put those 2 sheets together and tear them exactly in half. Then you have 4 sheets of paper. Continue this process of tearing and putting together for a total of 50 tears. If the paper is only $\dfrac{1}{1,000}$ of an inch thick, how many sheets of paper would there be? How thick or tall would the stack of paper be?

49

The Seesaw Problem

1. Eric and his little sister Amber enjoy playing on the seesaw at the playground. Amber weighs 65 pounds. Eric and Amber balance perfectly when Amber sits about 4 feet from the center and Eric sits about $2\frac{1}{2}$ feet from the center. About how much does Eric weigh?

2. Their little cousin Aleah joins them and sits with Amber. Can Eric balance the seesaw with both Amber and Aleah on one side, if Aleah weighs about the same as Amber? If so, where should he sit? If not, why not?

Nathan's Number Puzzles 1

Nathan has written pairs of linear sentences in symbols. Now he's trying to create word puzzles to go with them. Help him by creating a word puzzle for each pair of linear sentences below. Then find the numbers that fit his equations.

1. $x + 3y = 5$
   $3x + y = 7$

2. $x + 3y = 10$
   $3x + 14 = 2y$

3. $x + 2y = 7$
   $x + 2y = 17$

51

Systems of Linear Equations 1

Marika has asked you to help her understand how to solve systems of equations. Solve each system of equations below using a different strategy. Then explain to Marika why you chose that strategy for that system. Which are best solved by substitution? Which might be easily graphed? Which could be solved by elimination?

1. $y = x - 1$
    $3x - 4y = 8$

2. $3x + 2y = -10$
    $2x + 3y = 0$

3. $x + y = -10$
    $.5x + 1.5y = 5$

4. $3x - 2y = 6$
    $-2x + 3y = 0$

52

Systems of Linear Equations II

Amal is learning about systems of linear equations. He has come up with some questions regarding equations such as $y = 3x + 8$ and $y = -5x + 11$. Help him by answering the questions below.

1. What is the objective for solving a system of equations such as the one given?

2. How could you find the solution by graphing?

3. How could you find the solution by using tables of values?

4. How might you find the solution for the system without a graph or a table?

5. What would you look for in the table, the graph, or in the equations themselves that would indicate that a system of equations has no solution?

53

Nathan's Number Puzzles II

Nathan likes to make up puzzles about integers. Some of his recent puzzles are below. Write symbolic sentences that represent Nathan's puzzles. Then solve each puzzle.

1. Two numbers have a sum of 10. If you add the first number to twice the second number, the result is 8. What are the numbers?

2. One number is twice as large as a second number. The sum of the two numbers is 15. What are the numbers?

3. The first number minus the second number is 2. Twice the first number minus twice the second number is 4. What are the numbers?

Part 7: Functions

Overview

Grade 8

- Define, evaluate, and compare functions.
- Use functions to model relationships between quantities.

Slope-Intercept Equations I

Simplify the following equations so that you could enter them more easily into a graphing calculator. Give the slope and y-intercept for each without graphing it.

1. $y - 3(x - 7) = 5x$

2. $y = -2 + (x + 1)$

3. $y + 4 = \dfrac{5}{3}(x + 6)$

4. $y = 28 + 2.5(x - 6)$

5. $y = 13.2(x - 20) + 125.6$

How Long? How Far?

The Carmona family lives in Minnesota. They are driving to Florida for a vacation at an average speed of 60 miles per hour. Write an equation for a rule that can be used to calculate the distance they have traveled after any given number of hours. Then write a brief letter to the Carmona family that describes the advantages of having an equation, a table, and a graph to represent their situation.

56

Game Time

Abby and her brother Harry like to play a game called "U-Say, I-Say." Harry gives the "U-Say" number (an integer between −10 and +10). Abby has a secret rule she performs on the number that results in the "I-Say" number. Complete the table below by giving the missing "I-Say" values. Then describe Abby's rule in words and symbols.

U-Say	3	0	−4	1	2	5
I-Say	11	2	−10	5		

57

Hedwig's Hexagons

Hedwig is using toothpicks to build hexagon patterns. The first three are pictured. How do you think her pattern will continue? She has begun to collect information in a table in order to explore the relationships among the number of toothpicks, the number of hexagons, and the length of the outside perimeter of the figure. Complete the table for her.

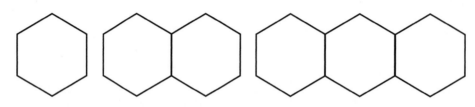

Number of toothpicks	6		
Number of hexagons	1	2	
Perimeter of figure	6	10	

58

Now write an equation for the relationship between the number of hexagons in each figure and the perimeter of the figure. Write another equation for the relationship between the number of hexagons and the number of toothpicks.

Slope-Intercept Equations II

Find an equation written in slope-intercept form that satisfies each condition below.

1. a line whose slope is −3 and passes through the point (2, 5)

2. a line whose slope is $\dfrac{-2}{3}$ and passes through the point (4, −1)

3. a line that passes through the points (2, 6) and (6, 1)

4. a line that passes through the points (−2, 3) and (4, −3)

5. a line that passes through the points (−1, −1) and (−5, −5)

59

Up and Down the Line I

Write an equation for the line pictured in each graph below.

1.

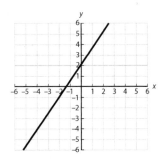

2.

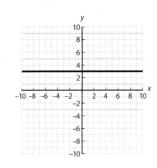

3.

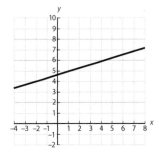

4.

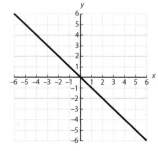

Up and Down the Line II

Write a linear equation for each condition below.

1.

x	−1	0	1	2	3
y	1	3	5	7	9

2. a line whose slope is −3 and y-intercept is 5

3. a line that passes through the points (2, 5) and (5, 6)

4. a line that passes through the point (3, 7) and has a slope of $\frac{2}{3}$

61

Butler Bake Sale

The Butler Middle School eighth grade class is planning a bake sale as a fall fund-raiser. Luis is chairing the planning committee. He gave a brief survey to determine what price should be charged for each brownie. He predicts from his results that a price of $0.50 per brownie will result in 200 brownies sold. He also predicts that a price of $1.00 per brownie will result in about 50 brownies sold. He is assuming that the relationship between the brownie price and the number sold is a linear relationship.

1. Write an equation for the relationship that Luis has predicted between the cost and the number of brownies sold.

2. Find the slope and y-intercept. Then explain what these mean in the context of Luis's information.

3. What if the committee decides to charge $0.70 per brownie? How many can they expect to sell?

4. Luis has taken an inventory and found that the class has 300 brownies to sell. Using your equation, what would be an appropriate price to charge for each brownie?

Looking for Lines

Explain how you can find the equation of a line if you know the information below. Use examples to explain your thinking.

1. the slope and y-intercept

2. two points on the line

3. the slope of the line and a point that is on the line, but is not the y-intercept

63

Thinking About Equations of Linear Models

Think about ways to find an equation of the form $y = mx + b$ or $y = a + bx$ from a table of data or a graph of the points. How can you find the equation if you know the slope and y-intercept? How can you find the graph by looking for the rate of change and other values from the table? How can you find the equation of the line if the slope and y-intercept are not given? Write a few sentences to explain your thinking.

64

Thinking About Change and Intercepts in Linear Models

Think about linear models in various forms. How can you see or find the rate of change in a linear model from a table of values? How would you find it from the graph? How does it appear in the equation? How would you determine the y-intercept in those three situations? Write a few sentences to explain your thinking.

65

Freezing or Boiling?

Lucas knows that the relationship between Celsius and Fahrenheit temperatures is a linear one. However, he often forgets the equation. He remembers that at freezing, the temperatures are (0°C, 32°F). At boiling, the respective temperatures are (100°C, 212°F). Explain to Lucas how he can find this equation knowing that the relationship is a linear one.

66

Border Tiles II

Landscapers often use square tiles as borders for garden plots and pools. The drawings below represent square pools for goldfish surrounded by 1-foot square tiles. For example, if the square pool is 2 × 2, there are 12 tiles in the border. If the square pool is 3 × 3, there are 16 square tiles in the border.

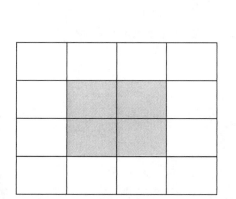 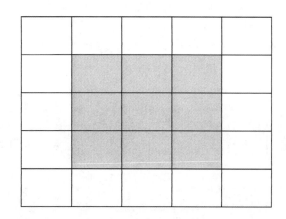

Collect data for a number of different-sized square pools. How many square tiles would be in the border around a pool that is 5 × 5? A pool that is 10 × 10? What patterns do you see in your data? Show and explain your thinking. Graph the data that you have collected. Then describe your graph.

Daily Warm-Ups: Pre-Algebra, Common Core State Standards

67

Table Patterns

Look at the tables below. For each table, do the following:

a. Describe symbolically or in words the pattern hiding in the table.

b. Give the missing values in the table.

c. Tell whether the relationship between x and y in the table is quadratic, linear, inverse, or exponential, or if it's some other type of relationship. Explain how you know.

1.

x	−1	0	1	2	3	4	5
y	5	7	9	11	13		

2.

x	0	1	2	3	4	5
y	1	2	5	10		

68

Parachuting Down

Cecelia took her first parachute jump lesson last weekend. Her instructor gave her the graph below that shows her change in altitude in meters during a 2-second interval. Use the graph to answer the questions that follow.

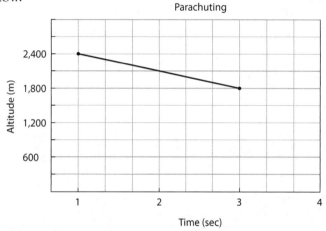

1. What is the slope of the line segment?

2. Estimate Cecelia's average rate of change in altitude in meters per second.

3. Give the domain and range for this graph.

Sketching a Graph

Sketch a graph that represents each situation below. Identify your variables and label the axes of your graph accordingly.

1. Edgar is paddling his kayak down the reservoir to visit a friend. For half an hour, he paddled slowly, enjoying the morning. Then he noticed that the weather might be changing and increased his speed. After another 10 minutes, the wind picked up. For about 20 minutes, the wind blew in the direction he was paddling. Then it shifted and blew directly into his face for the last 15 minutes.

2. An ice cream shop keeps track of ice cream sales using a graph. Sales are higher during warm weather and lower during cool weather. The shop opens its doors every year on the first day of spring. This year, the first few days of spring were very cold and rainy. Then, the weather slowly warmed each day and the days stayed dry. After three weeks, the weather turned colder again and it was cloudy for a week and a half.

Interpreting Graphs I

Which graph best represents the given situation? Be prepared to justify your answers.

1. A commuter train pulls into a station and drops off all its passengers.

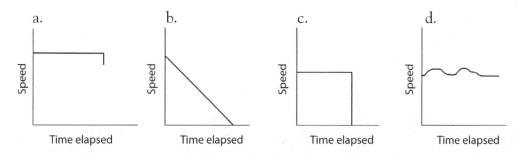

2. A child walks to a slide, climbs up to the top, and then slides down.

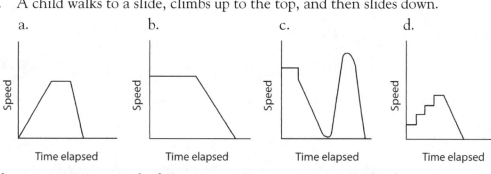

Daily Warm-Ups: Pre-Algebra, Common Core State Standards

Interpreting Graphs II

Which graph best represents the given situation? Be prepared to justify your answers.

1. A little boy swings on a swing at a playground.

a.   b.   c.   d.

 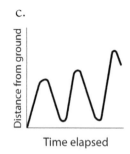 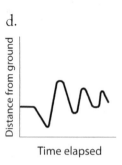

2. A woman walks up a hill at a constant rate and then runs down the other side.

a.   b.   c.   d.

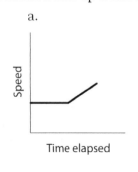 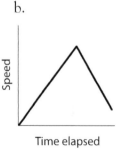 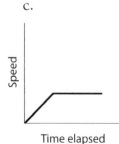 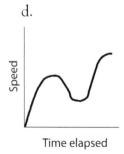

Ferris Wheel Graphs

Enrique took a ride on a Ferris wheel at the amusement park last weekend. He has sketched these graphs to represent that ride. Which one best represents the idea that he's trying to show? Explain why you chose that graph.

a.

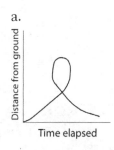

b.

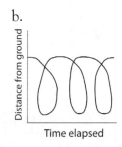

c.

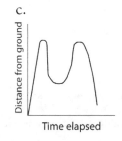

d.

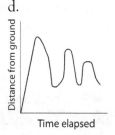

Roller Coaster Ride

Marjorie and Jack love to ride roller coasters and then portray their ride in a graph. Last Saturday, they rode the Mighty Twister and sketched this graph of that experience.

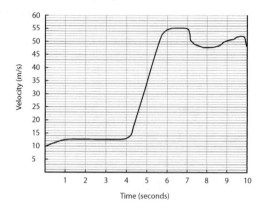

1. What does the pattern of their graph tell you about when they were going down the steepest hill?

2. What was their approximate velocity 1 second into the ride? What was their velocity 8 seconds into the ride?

3. After getting started, when were they going the slowest? The fastest?

4. Describe what was happening to them between 4 and 8 seconds.

Daily Warm-Ups: Pre-Algebra, Common Core State Standards

Graphing People Over Time

Think about each situation below. Then sketch a graph to represent the situation over a 24-hour period of time. Label each graph carefully using the horizontal axis to represent the time of day. Be prepared to explain and justify your choices.

1. the number of people at a very popular pizza restaurant on a Saturday

2. the number of people in a school building on a weekday in September

3. the number of people at a sports stadium on the day of a big game

4. the number of people at a movie theater on a weekend day

75

Renting Canoes

Dan and Julia have reservations for 10 students for the Outdoor Adventure Club's annual trip. This year they are planning a canoe camping trip. The Otter Mountain River Livery rents canoe and camping gear for $19 per person. Dan and Julia expect no more than 50 students in all to go on the trip. Using increments of 10 campers, make a table showing the total rental charge for 10 to 50 campers. Then make a coordinate graph of the data.

76

Grow Baby!

The average growth weight in pounds of a baby born in the United States is a function of the baby's age in months. Look at the sample data provided and graph the information in an appropriate window. Then write two sentences about the graph and the relationship between the two variables.

Age in months	Weight in pounds
0	7
3	13
6	17
9	20
12	22
15	24
18	25
21	26
24	27

Daily Warm-Ups: Pre-Algebra, Common Core State Standards

77

Part 8: Geometry

Overview

Grade 6

- Solve real-world and mathematical problems involving area, surface area, and volume.

Grade 7

- Solve real-life and mathematical problems involving angle measure, area, surface area, and volume.

Grade 8

- Solve real-world and mathematical problems involving volume of cylinders, cones, and spheres.

An Unusual Area

Vachon is helping his uncle tile a patio that has an unusual shape. He has drawn a sketch on grid paper to represent the area that they need to cover. Each unit on the grid paper represents 2 feet. Find the area of the figure, and explain your strategy.

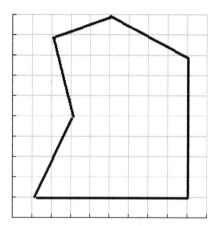

Areas of Triangles

Give the base, the height, and the area of each triangle pictured below. Are the triangles congruent? Explain your thinking.

1.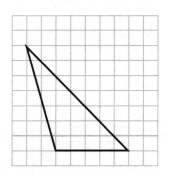

2.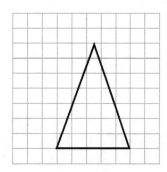

3.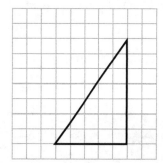

Considering Pizza Costs

Paisano's Pizza Parlor has just opened up across the street from Mei's apartment. Mei is thinking about inviting some friends over for pizza and ordering from Paisano's. She wants to get the most pizza for her money. The menu shows the following prices:

> 6-inch round pizza..................$7.50
>
> 12-inch round pizza................$12.00
>
> 18-inch round pizza................$16.00

1. How many 6-inch pizzas have the same amount of pizza as one 12-inch pizza?

2. How many 6-inch pizzas have the same amount of pizza as one 18-inch pizza?

Pondering Pizza Prices

Antonio is the new owner of Paisano's Pizza Parlor. He wants to change the way his pizzas are priced. He is thinking about pricing them according to the diameter of each pizza. His cousin Vinnie recommends that he price them according to the size of the circumference of each pizza. His wife Bianca suggests pricing by the area of each pizza. Which method would you recommend to Antonio? Explain your reasoning.

81

Circles and Squares

Find the area of the shaded region for each figure below.

1.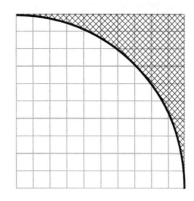

2.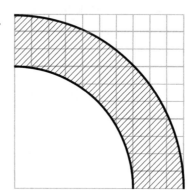

Perimeter Expressions

Rajah is working on her math homework. She has been given the sketch below, where r represents both the radius of the semicircle and the height of the rectangle that the semicircle is attached to. She is trying to decide on an expression that will represent the perimeter of the figure. She has written out the expressions below. Do they correctly represent the perimeter of the shape? Explain why or why not for each.

1. $r(2 + \pi)$

2. $4r + \pi r$

3. $r + 2r + r + 2\pi r$

4. $r(4 + \pi)$

5. $2r + \pi r$

Cynthia's Cylinder

Cynthia has drawn the model below to represent a cylindrical cardboard box that she needs to package a gift of lotion for her mother. If the package needs to be 8 inches tall and have a diameter of 3 inches, what is the area of the rectangle pictured? What is the total surface area of the box that she will create from her design?

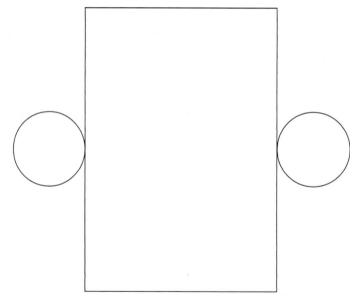

84

© 2012 Walch Education

Volume and Surface Area I

The drawing below is a flat pattern or a net. When folded, it creates a box in the shape of a rectangular prism. Draw a sketch of the box and determine its total surface area and volume.

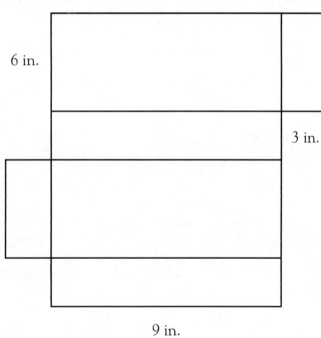

6 in.

3 in.

9 in.

85

Volume and Surface Area II

The drawing below represents an open-topped rectangular prism with a length of 13 feet, a height of 6 feet, and a width of 5 feet. Draw a flat pattern or a net for the figure. Determine the surface area and volume of the box.

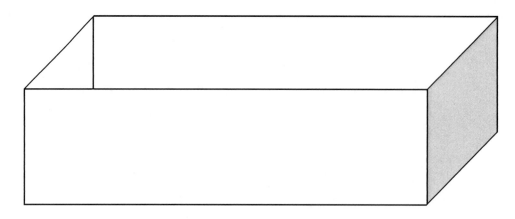

A Rectangular Box

1. Make a sketch of a rectangular box with a base of 3 inches by 5 inches and a height of 7 inches. How many unit cubes would fit in a single layer at the bottom of the box?

2. How many identical layers of unit cubes could be stacked in the box?

3. What is the volume and surface area of the box?

87

Area and Perimeter

The figure below represents a rectangle with a length of 48 centimeters and a height of 16 centimeters. A semicircle with a radius of 8 centimeters has been cut out of each end of the rectangle. Find the area and perimeter of the shaded region of the figure.

88

Storing DVDs

Malik wants to make an open-top cardboard box to fit on a certain shelf in his closet to store his DVD collection. He has drawn the sketch below of the box that he needs.

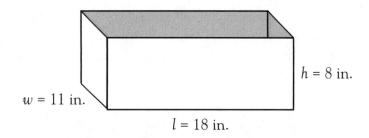

w = 11 in.

h = 8 in.

l = 18 in.

1. How much cardboard will Malik need to create this box?

2. If a typical DVD package measures 7.5 inches × 5.25 inches × 0.5 inches, how many DVDs can Malik expect to store in the box he makes?

3. Malik's dad has brought him a piece of cardboard that measures 2 feet by 3 feet. Is this enough cardboard for the project? Could Malik cut all the pieces that he needs? Explain why or why not.

89

Daily Warm-Ups: Pre-Algebra, Common Core State Standards

Storing Trash

According to the U.S. Environmental Protection Agency, U.S. residents, businesses, and institutions made more than 236 million tons of solid municipal waste in 2003. Every ton of waste takes up 2.5 cubic yards of space. Andrew and Todd are wondering how many math classrooms like theirs would be needed to store all that garbage. Their classroom is 45 feet long, 30 feet wide, and 12 feet tall. How many rooms would be needed to store the garbage?

90

Beach Volleyball

Beach volleyball is played on beaches around the world and is a growing sport in the United States and Canada. The ball used for beach volleyball is a little larger in diameter than a traditional volleyball. It is usually brightly colored compared to the white ball used in indoor games. The Victor Volleyball Company packages its individual beach volleyballs in display cartons that measure 1 foot on each edge. It then ships 12 boxed volleyballs per carton to sporting goods stores all over the world.

1. Find the dimensions of all the different possible shipping cartons that the Victor Volleyball Company could use for exactly 12 balls.

2. Find the surface area of each shipping carton.

3. Which carton needs the least amount of cardboard?

4. Imagine that the Victor Volleyball Company has a greater demand for volleyballs and decides to package 24 boxed volleyballs in a carton. How much packaging material will the company need to create the box with the least material? How much more material is this than the least amount needed for shipping 12 balls?

Tree Dilemma

Eric's neighbor wants to cut down a dead tree that is in his yard. Eric is worried that when the tree is cut, it will fall on his garage, which is 42 feet from the tree. His neighbor decides to measure the height of the tree by using its shadow. The tree's shadow measures 47.25 feet. At the same time, Eric puts a yardstick next to the tree, and the yardstick casts a shadow of 3.5 feet. Will the tree hit Eric's garage if it falls the wrong way? Explain carefully. Include a sketch of the situation to help clarify your thinking.

92

Road Trip

1. Two cars leave the same parking lot in Centerville at noon. One travels due north, and the other travels directly east. Suppose the northbound car is traveling at 60 mph and the eastbound car is traveling at 50 mph. Make a table that shows the distance each car has traveled and the distance between the two cars after 1 hour, 2 hours, 3 hours, and so forth. Describe how the distances are changing.

2. Suppose the northbound car is traveling at 40 mph, and after 2 hours the two cars are 100 miles apart. How fast is the other car going?

3. Draw a diagram to help explain the situation. Explain your thinking clearly.

93

Comparing Cylinders

Two cylinders are pictured below. All the dimensions of cylinder A are 3 times the dimensions of cylinder B.

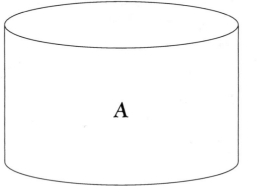

1. What is the ratio of the radius of cylinder A to the radius of cylinder B?

2. What is the ratio of the height of cylinder A to the height of cylinder B?

3. What is the ratio of the surface area of cylinder A to the surface area of cylinder B?

4. What is the ratio of the volume of cylinder A to the volume of cylinder B?

Concession Concern

Emile and Sharonda are in charge of concessions for their school's football games. They usually sell popcorn in cylindrical containers like the one below on the right. However, they have just noticed that their supply of these containers is gone, and there's no time to get more before the next game. Emile notices that there are plenty of the cone-shaped containers like the one on the left. He suggests that they use those. Both of the containers have a height of 8 inches and a radius of 3 inches.

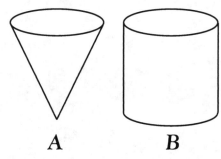

A   **B**

1. What is the difference between what the cone will hold and what the cylinder will hold?

2. If Emile and Sharonda usually charge $1.50 for the cylinder full of popcorn, what should they charge for the cone?

Popcorn Pricing

Twin sisters Elizabeth and Emma enjoy going to the movies on Saturday afternoons. Sometimes they each buy a small popcorn for $3.00, and sometimes they buy a large popcorn that costs $6.00 and share it. Both containers are cylinders. The heights of the two containers are the same. However, the radius of the large container is about twice the radius of the small container. Which purchase gives the sisters the most popcorn for their money? Draw a sketch of the two popcorn containers, and explain your thinking.

96

Juice Packaging

The Johnny Appleseed Juice Company is changing its packaging. The juice currently comes in a cylindrical container like the one pictured below on the right. The company is considering changing this container to a prism. The prism will have a square base that has the same width as the diameter of the cylinder, which is 5 inches. The height of both containers is $7\frac{1}{2}$ inches.

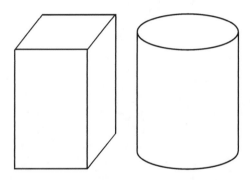

1. What is the volume of each container?

2. If the company was charging $3.29 for the cylindrical container of juice, what would be a fair price to charge for the new container?

Cylinder Expressions

The cylinder below has a base area of 45 cm². It is partially filled with liquid up to a height of x cm. The height from the top of the liquid to the top of the cylinder is represented by y cm. The total height is represented by h cm. Which expressions below properly represent the total volume of the cylinder?

a. $45(h - x)$

b. $45(x + y)$

c. $45x + 45y$

d. $45xy$

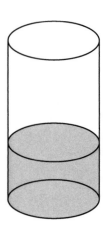

Paper Cylinders

Erica has a sheet of paper that is $8\frac{1}{2}$ inches by 11 inches. Without cutting the paper, she wants to make a container with the greatest possible volume. (She will make the top and bottom of the container with another sheet of paper.) She thought of rolling the paper to make an open-ended cylinder and realized that there are two ways to do this. Her friend Aleah suggests folding the paper to make a rectangular prism with square ends instead. Erica points out that there are also two ways to fold the paper to make the sides of a prism with a square base.

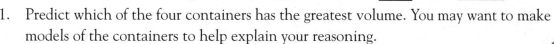

1. Predict which of the four containers has the greatest volume. You may want to make models of the containers to help explain your reasoning.

2. Now find the volume of each container. What is the volume of the largest container?

3. How much greater is the volume of that container than the volume of the other container of the same height?

4. Write a note to Erica that explains and justifies your thinking clearly.

Daily Warm-Ups: Pre-Algebra, Common Core State Standards

Tennis Ball Packaging

Rochelle works as a packaging engineer for the Creative Carton Company. The company wants to remove the air from containers of tennis balls so the balls will retain a good bounce. Rochelle needs to know how much air there is in a standard container of tennis balls. Help Rochelle by finding the amount of empty space in a cylindrical container that is 18 centimeters tall and contains 3 tennis balls that are each 6 centimeters in diameter. Then write a note to her about how you found your answer.

100

Part 9: Statistics and Probability

Overview

Grade 7

- Investigate chance processes and develop, use, and evaluate probability models.

Grade 8

- Investigate patterns of association in bivariate data.

Ring Toss

Shareen and her brother Samir like to go to carnivals and fairs in the summertime. They enjoy the games and the rides. One day, they watched a ring-toss game in which there were old glass soda bottles standing on a wooden platform. The attendant was encouraging Samir to play the game. He said that Samir had a 50% chance of getting any ring to fall over a bottle because the ring will either go on the bottle or fall off. Do you think that Samir and Shareen should believe the attendant? Why or why not? Explain your thinking.

101

Coin Chances

1. Alicia tossed a quarter 5 times in a row. It landed tails up 5 times in a row. What is the probability that it will land tails up when she tosses it again? Explain your thinking.

2. Daryl has 5 coins worth exactly 27 cents in his pocket. What is the probability that 1 coin is a quarter? What is the probability that 3 coins are nickels?

3. Make up another probability question about Daryl's coins. Provide the answer, and be ready to explain your thinking.

102

Daily Warm-Ups: Pre-Algebra, Common Core State Standards

Pairing Socks

Jamal does not like to take the time to pair his socks after he takes them out of the dryer, so he just throws them into his sock drawer. He knows he has 4 black socks, 2 blue socks, 2 white socks, and 2 tan socks in his sock drawer. One morning he needs to dress in a hurry and wants to wear his tan socks. Without turning on his bedroom light, he reaches in and pulls out one sock.

1. What is the probability that the sock he pulls out is tan?

2. What is the probability that he will get a black or a blue sock on the first try?

3. If he pulls out a tan sock the first time, what is the probability that he will get a tan sock on his next try?

4. What is the probability that Jamal will get a matching pair of socks of any color if he makes two successive selections?

Tossing Coins

1. If you toss a nickel and a dime together, what is the sample space (or all the possible results that you could get)?

2. What is the probability that you would get heads for the nickel and tails for the dime on the same toss?

3. What is the probability that one coin will be heads and one will be tails?

4. What is the probability that *at least* one coin will be tails?

104

Ice Cream Cones

Frosty Freeze features 9 different ice cream flavors each Wednesday. How many different 2-scoop cones could you order if you did not repeat flavors? What if you allowed for 2 scoops of the same flavor as well? Justify your thinking. What if the order of scoops matters? What if order does not matter?

105

Spinning for Numbers

Look at the spinner below. If it is spun, find each probability given.

1. P(a factor of 12)

2. P(a multiple of 3)

3. P(9)

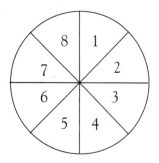

4. P(a prime number)

5. P(an even number)

6. P(neither a prime nor a composite number)

106

Analyzing Scatter Plots

Ashley is reviewing the results of data collected and graphed from three different experiments. Help her by describing the patterns you see in these graphs. If appropriate, draw lines that you think might fit the data. If you don't think that a line fits the data, explain why.

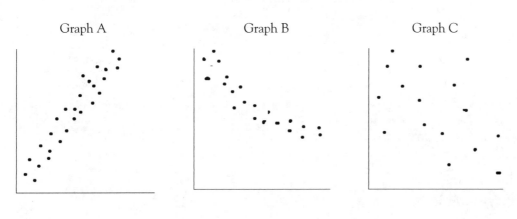

Graph A   Graph B   Graph C

Mr. Wiley's Baby

Mr. Wiley presented some data to his algebra class about the early growth of his new baby boy. Hayley created a scatter plot for Mr. Wiley's data. The data and scatter plot are shown at right.

Week	Weight
1	8.5
2	9.25
3	9.75
4	9.75
5	10.5
6	11
7	11.5
8	11.75

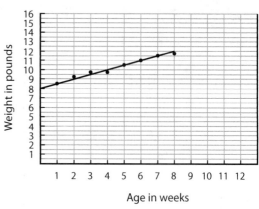

1. Does the data seem to represent a linear model? What equation fits Hayley's graph model?

2. How long do you suppose this growth pattern will continue in this way? If it does continue, what would you expect Mr. Wiley's son to weigh in 1 year? In 2 years? In 14 years?

3. Within what age limits do you think this is a reasonable representation of the growth of Mr. Wiley's baby?

108

Answer Key

Part 1: Operations and Algebraic Thinking

1. 6, 28, and 496 are perfect numbers.

2. There were 301 T-shirts. Students will likely use least common multiples of 4, 5, and 6 that are divisible by 7.

3. 1. Rectangles of 36 and 48 square yards will have the most configurations because they have more pairs of factors.

   2. 36 and 49 will have square configurations.

4. Garrett can make 8 different configurations: 1 × 144, 2 × 72, 3 × 48, 4 × 36, 6 × 24, 8 × 18, 9 × 16, and 12 × 12. These represent pairs of factors.

Part 2: Number and Operations—Fractions

5. The fraction 7/8 is larger. Brigit's strategy: 7/8 = .875; 2/3 = .666

Jordan's strategy:

Jose's strategy:

Answer Key

6. 1. $\frac{7}{10}$, $\frac{13}{20}$. In addition to equivalent-fraction procedures, students could use fraction strips or fraction circles to show the relationships between the fractions.
   2. Students might use fraction strips or circles to show that $\frac{11}{12}$ leaves the smallest remainder in the whole unit, and therefore is the larger fraction.

7. Max is right. Possible thinking: Both $\frac{3}{4}$ and $\frac{2}{3}$ are greater than $\frac{1}{2}$, so the result should be greater than 1, but $\frac{5}{7}$ is less than 1. Students also might discuss the common denominator equaling 12.

8. Students should give examples of multiplying and dividing with fractions to show that sometimes multiplication results in smaller products and division results in larger quotients than the number originally being multiplied or divided.

Part 3: Measurement and Data

9. 1. $15 \times 21 = 315/9 = 35$ square yards $\times$ \$7.32 = \$256.20
   2. $(15 + 21)2 = 72$ feet; $72/8 = 9$ pieces of molding $\times$ \$134.00 = \$1,206

10. There are five unique rectangles: 1×48, 2×24, 3×16, 4×12, 6×8. The smallest perimeter is 28 units for the 6×8 rectangle. The largest perimeter is 98 units for the 1×48 rectangle. None are perfect squares.

11. Yes, there's room for 5 pairs. They require 15 to 20 square feet. 12 pairs would require 36 to 48 square feet. To provide the maximum space, Kanya and her father could increase the depth by 4 feet or the width by 6 feet.

Part 4: Ratios and Proportional Relationships

12. Students could scale to 60 roses, which yields \$75 and \$69 respectively, or find the price per rose, which yields \$1.25 and \$1.15 respectively. Thus, 20 roses for \$23.00 is the better buy per rose.

13. There will be no remainder. The friends predict that they will eat 110% of the pizza (10% + 50% + 35% + 15% = 110%), so there won't be enough.

14. The 18-inch pizza provides the best value. 9-inch pizza: 63.6 square inches/10.5 = 6.06 square inches per \$1.00; 12-inch pizza: 113.1 square inches/15 = 7.54 square inches per \$1.00; 18-inch pizza: 254.5 square inches/19 = 13.39 square inches per \$1.00

Answer Key

15. 3.44 miles per hour
16. The original area on the grid is approximately 52 square units. The new area is approximately 34 square units. This represents a 34.6% decrease in area.
17. 1. growth; ratio = 3; 300% increase
    2. growth; ratio = 1.1; 110% increase
    3. decay; ratio = .6; 60% decrease
    4. decay; ratio = .2; 20% decrease
    5. decay; ratio = .38; 38% decrease
18. 1. 32%
    2. $1.37/loaf
    3. The 2010 price is 32% greater. If the trend were continuing, one might assume that the percent increase would be closer to 16%.

Part 5: The Number System

19. Veronica can make 9 bows, with $\frac{1}{3}$ yard remaining.
20. 45 pies (or 44, depending on rounding)
21. 1. 25 students would get a portion with $\frac{1}{4}$ remaining.
    2. 17 students would get a portion.
    3. Students should use drawings of the sub divided into appropriate length portions.

22. Anatole was born on a Saturday. 759/7 = 108 R3
23. The GCF is 12. Find the prime factorization of each number and compare. Then take the product of the common factors.
24. They will all be there again in 300 days; this number represents the least common multiple (LCM).
25. 1. 221 years
    2. 336 years
    3. The answer represents the LCM.
26. Answers will vary. Sample answers: (12 + 34) + (5 × 6) + 7 + 8 + 9 = 100; 123 − 4 − 5 − 6 − 7 + 8 − 9 = 100
27. 1.

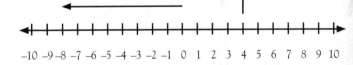

Daily Warm-Ups: Pre-Algebra, Common Core State Standards

Answer Key

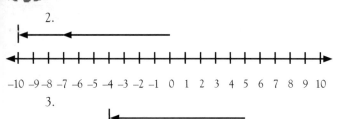

2.

3.

28. 1. $(-9) + 7 = (-2)$
    2. $(-4) + (-6) = (-10)$
    3. $7 + (-14) = -7$
29. 1. $5 + (-8) = (-3)$
    2. $(-6) + 10 = 4$
    3. $(-8) + 3 = (-5)$
30. 1. Chip board 1: 5 black chips; Chip board 2: 5 black chips and 9 white chips; Chip board 3: 4 white chips
    2. Chip board 1: 12 white chips; Chip board 2: 12 white chips and 7 black chips; Chip board 3: 5 white chips

3. Chip board 1: 8 black chips; Chip board 2: 5 black chips crossed out or removed; Chip board 3 (or 2): 3 black chips
31. Chip board 1 should have 6 black chips. Chip board 2 could show the 6 black chips with 6 "zeros" included. Chip board 3 would show 6 white chips remain after 12 black chips are removed. So, $(-6) - (-12) = +6$.
32. 1. -18
    2. 33
    3. -21
    4. -5
    5. $-1/4$
    6. 7
    7. -2
    8. -5
    9. -7
    10. -2.2
    11. $-3\frac{1}{5}$
    12. $187/10$

Answer Key

33. 1. $\frac{60}{100} = \frac{6}{10} = \frac{3}{5} = 0.6 = 60\%$

    2. $\frac{55}{100} = \frac{11}{20} = 0.55 = 55\%$

34. $0.3 \times 0.4 = 0.12$; $\frac{3}{10} \times \frac{4}{10} = \frac{12}{100}$; 30% of 40% is 12%

35. $1 = \frac{4}{4} - (4-4)$; $2 = \frac{4}{4} + \frac{4}{4}$; $3 = \frac{(4+4+4)}{4}$;

    $4 = (4-4) \times 4 + 4$; $5 = (4 \times 4 + 4)/4$; $6 = (4+4)/4 + 4$;

    $7 = (4+4) - 4/4$; $8 = 4 + 4 + 4 - 4$; $9 = 4 + 4 + 4/4$;

    $10 = (44 - 4)/4$

36. There are 1,024 pages: 9 one-digit pages, 90 two-digit pages, 900 three-digit pages, and 25 four-digit pages.

37. 1,568 students; $(791 \times 2) - (2 \times 7) = 1{,}568$

38. $4.6 \times 0.75 = 3.45 \times 4 \times 365 = 5{,}037$ pounds/50 = 100.7 cubic feet

39.

$$\sqrt{17}\ \sqrt{24}\ \sqrt{35} \qquad\qquad \sqrt{96}$$

(number line from 0 to 10)

Part 6: Expressions and Equations

40. Students should get 6 each time.

    $\{[n + (n+1) + 11]/2\} - n = 6$

41. 1. Drawings will vary, but should reflect the pattern.

    2. 15 orange creams; $(R-1)(C-1)$ = number of orange creams for R rows and C columns of French mints

42. 1. -3

    2. $-5\frac{1}{2}$

    3. 128

    4. 4.75

    5. 0

    6. 72

    7. 1

    8. 16

    9. 2

    10. 50

43. 1. 24

    2. 10

    3. 413

    4. 24

    5. 12.5

6. -90
7. 3/4
8. 0
9. 0
10. -40

44. Maria may be counting all the tiles at the top and bottom of the border $(n + 2)$ and then adding the remaining tiles on each side (n) for her expression. Carlos may be thinking that the border can be separated into 4 equal sets of $(n + 1)$ sections.

45. Answers will vary. Sample answer: Sam needs $\frac{2}{3}$ yard of fabric to make an apron. If she has 5 yards of fabric, how many aprons can she make? She can make 7 aprons with a $\frac{1}{2}$ yard remaining.

46. 1. $2(5) + 2(4) + 4(2.5) = 28$ meters
    2. $P = 2M + 2N + 4L = 2(M + N) + 4L$
    3. Answers will vary.

47. 1. $S = 4L + 4W + 4H = 4(L + W + H)$
    2. $A = 2LW + 2LH + 2WH = 2(LW + LH + WH)$

48. 1. $8x - 40$ or $4(2x - 10)$
    2. $5x^2 - 6x + 13x - 10 = 5x^2 + 7x - 10$
    3. $4x + 20 - 6 + 12x = 16x + 14$
    4. $30 - 5x + 5x + 5 = 35$
    5. $-5x^2 + 3x + 5$ or $5(1 - x^2) + 3x$

49. $2^{50} = 1.125899907 \times 10^{15}$ sheets of paper $/1,000 = 1.125899907 \times 10^{12}$ inches $/12 = 9.382499224 \times 10^{10}$ feet $/5,280 = 17,769,884.89$ miles

50. 1. Eric weighs about 104 pounds.
    2. If Amber and Aleah continue to sit at 4 feet, then $130 \times 4 = 104 \times D$, and $D = 5$ feet. If the seesaw is long enough, then Eric can balance them. Otherwise, he cannot.

51. Word puzzles will vary.
    1. $(2, 1)$
    2. $(-2, 4)$
    3. not possible

52. Students' choices and rationales may vary.
    1. $(-4, -5)$
    2. $(-6, 4)$
    3. $(-20, 10)$
    4. $(3.6, 2.4)$

Answer Key

53. Answers will vary.
    1. Sample answer: to find an ordered pair that satisfies both equations
    2. Sample answer: Graph both lines on the same set of axes, and locate the intersection point of the two lines.
    3. Sample answer: Substitute values of x into both equations. Look for identical y values for the same value of x.
    4. Sample answer: solve algebraically by substitution or elimination
    5. Sample answer: If the values in the table have the same constant rate of change, if the lines are parallel, or if the slopes are the same but have different y-intercepts, then there is no solution.
54. 1. $x + y = 10$; $x + 2y = 8$; $(12, -2)$
    2. $x + 2y$; $x + y = 15$; $(10, 5)$
    3. $x - y = 2$; $2x - 2y = 4$; Any values for x and y that differ by 2 will work in this puzzle. There are infinite solutions.

Part 7: Functions

55. 1. $y = 8x - 21$; slope = 8, y-intercept = $(0, 21)$
    2. $y = x - 1$; slope = 1, y-intercept = $(0, -1)$
    3. $y = \frac{5}{3}x + 6$; slope = 5/3, y-intercept = $(0, 6)$
    4. $y = 2.5x + 13$; slope = 5/2, y-intercept = $(0, 13)$
    5. $y = 13.2x - 138.4$; slope = 66/5, y-intercept = $(0, -138.4)$
56. $D = 60t$. Letters will vary.
57.

U-Say	3	0	-4	1	2	5
I-Say	11	2	-10	5	8	17

Abby's rule: I-Say = 3 • U-Say + 2

58.

Number of toothpicks	6	11	16
Number of hexagons	1	2	3
Perimeter of figure	6	10	14

$T = 5H + 1$; $P = 4H + 2$

59. 1. $y = -3x + 11$
    2. $y = -\frac{2}{3}x + \frac{5}{3}$
    3. $y = -\frac{5}{4}x + \frac{17}{2}$
    4. $y = -x + 1$
    5. $y = x + 0$

Daily Warm-Ups: Pre-Algebra, Common Core State Standards

Answer Key

60. 1. $y = \frac{3}{2}x + 2$

 2. $y = 3$

 3. The line passes through $(1, 5)$ and $(4, 6)$, thus
 $y = \frac{1}{3}x + \frac{14}{3}$.

 4. $y = -x$

61. 1. $y = 2x + 3$

 2. $y = -3x + 5$

 3. $(y - 5) = \frac{1}{3}(x - 2)$

 4. $(y - 7) = \frac{2}{3}(x - 3)$

62. 1. $y = -300x + 350$ for x = cost and y = number sold

 2. The slope = -300, and the y-intercept = 350. For every $1.00 increase in price, the number sold decreases by 300; in addition, they can give away 350 brownies if they don't charge anything.

 3. 140 brownies

 4. about $0.17 for each brownie

63. Answers will vary.

64. Answers will vary. Sample answer: If you know the slope and y-intercept, you can substitute the values into the equation $y = mx + b$ or $y = a + bx$. The slope can be determined from the graph by finding the change in y divided by the change in x. The y-intercept will be the point where $x = 0$ in the table and where the line crosses the y-axis on the graph.

65. Answers will vary. Sample answer: The rate of change is the value found when the difference in two y values is divided by the difference in the corresponding two x values, either from the table or from the graph using any two points. In the equation, the rate of change is the value m or b when the equation is written in the form $y = mx + b$ or $y = a + bx$. The y-intercept is the value $(0, x)$.

66. Slope is $\frac{212 - 32}{100 - 0} = \frac{180}{100} = \frac{9}{5}$, thus $y = \frac{9}{5}x + 32$.
 Note: y = Fahrenheit and x = Celsius.

Answer Key

67.

Side of pool	Number of border tiles
2	12
3	16
4	20
5	24
6	28
7	32

Tiles increase by 4: $B = 4S + 4$.
The graph is a straight line.

68. 1. a. $y = 2x + 7$; As x increases, y increases by a
   constant amount. First differences are constant.
   b. missing values: (4, 15) (5, 17)
   c. The relationship is linear.

2. a. $y = -x^2 + 11x$; As x increases, y increases by
   a decreasing amount. Second differences are
   constant.
   b. missing values: (4, 28) (5, 30)
   c. The relationship is quadratic.

69. 1. slope = $-600/2$ or -300
2. rate of change = 300 mps downward
3. The domain for the line segment is $1 \le s \le 3$. The
   range for the line segment is $1{,}800 \le A \le 2{,}400$.

70. 1.

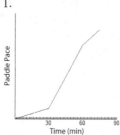

2.

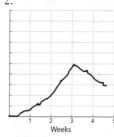

71. 1. b
2. c

72. 1. c
2. a

73. Students should choose to justify choice *c* as the proper
graph.

74. 1. between 4 and 6 seconds
2. about 13 m/sec; 48 m/sec
3. from 1 to 4 seconds into the ride; 6 to 7 seconds
   into the ride
4. The velocity increased rapidly. They stayed at
   55 m/sec for 1 second, then decreased between
   7 and 8 seconds, increased to about 53 m/sec, and
   then began to decrease again.

Daily Warm-Ups: Pre-Algebra, Common Core State Standards

Answer Key

75. Graphs will vary depending on students' interpretations of the situations. Most students will create line or bar graphs. Discuss the appropriateness of a continuous or discrete graph for these models.

76.

People	Total charge
10	190
15	285
20	380
25	475
30	570
35	665
40	760
45	855
50	950

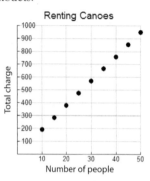

77. The weight increases more each month in the first year than in the second year. The graph looks like it might fit a parabolic curve for $0 \le x \le 25$.

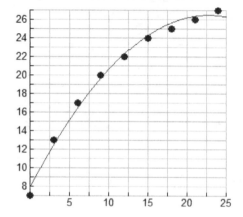

Quadratic regression
$regEQ(x) = -.035955x^2 + 1.63514x + 7.82424$

Part 8: Geometry

78. The area is approximately 220 square feet. The area can be found by separating the figure into rectangles and triangles.

79. For each triangle, $b = 5$, $h = 7$, and $A = 35$. They are not necessarily congruent; however, their areas are equal.

80. 1. One 12-inch pizza equals four 6-inch pizzas.
    2. One 18-inch pizza equals nine 6-inch pizzas.

81. An area pricing model would be best. Explanations will vary.

82. 1. $A = 100 - (100 \times 3.14/4) = 21.5$ square units
    2. $\{(100 \times 3.14) - 49 \times 3.14\}/4 = 40$ square units

83. 1. no
    2. yes
    3. no
    4. yes
    5. no
    Circumference of circle, c, is 2, but Rajah is given a semicircle. Hence, the circumference of the semicirle is πr. The rectangle has 3 sides to consider for the perimeter. The length is $2r$ and the height is r. Thus, the perimeter of the rectangle is $2h + 1 = 2r + 2r = 4r$. The total perimeter of the figure is $4r + \pi r$, or $r(4 + \pi)$.

84. area of rectangle = 75.36 square inches; total surface area = 89.52 square inches

85. surface area = 198 square in.; volume = 162 cubic in.

86. surface area = 261 square feet; volume = 390 cubic feet
    A possible net for the figure:

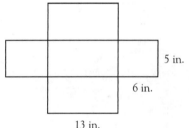

87. 1. 15 unit cubes
    2. 7 layers
    3. 105 in³; 142 in² (open box)

88. perimeter = 146.24 centimeters; area = 567.04 square centimeters

89. 1. 662 square inches
     2. 72 DVDs
     3. Yes; answers will vary.
90. classroom = 600 cubic yards; 236 million tons × 2.5 cubic yards divided by 600 cubic yards = 980,000 classrooms
91. 1. $1 \times 1 \times 12$; $1 \times 2 \times 6$; $1 \times 3 \times 4$; $2 \times 2 \times 3$
     2. 50 square feet; 40 square feet; 38 square feet; 32 square feet
     3. the carton that is $2 \times 2 \times 3$
     4. The carton that is $2 \times 3 \times 4$ needs 52 square feet of cardboard, 20 square feet more than a 12-ball carton.
92.

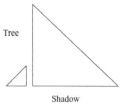

$$\frac{47.25}{3.5} = \frac{T}{3}, T = 40.5;$$ Eric's garage may be safe, but only by a foot and a half.

93. 1.

Time in hours	Northbound car's distance in miles	Eastbound car's distance in miles	Distance between cars in miles
1	60	50	78.1
2	120	100	156.2
3	180	150	234.3
4	240	200	312.4

Each car's distance from the starting point is increasing by the amount of its rate of speed each hour. The distance between the cars is increasing by 78.1 miles each hour.

2. $100^2 - 80^2 = 3,600$; thus, the other car traveled 60 miles in 2 hours at a rate of 30 mph.

3.

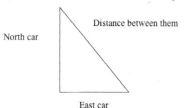

94. 1. 3:1
     2. 3:1
     3. 9:1
     4. 27:1